The New Club

by Winston White

illustrated by Cindy Revell

HOUGHTON MIFFLIN   BOSTON

Chapter 1

Every year, Morris School had Club Day. On Club Day, each of the school clubs set up a booth. Students could join any of the clubs they liked.

Ms. Cooper told her class, "Find a club that you want to join."

Hector, Lisa, and Tom stopped at the Art Club booth first.

"I really like to draw and paint," Lisa said. "I'm joining this club."

Hector and Tom kept looking.

Tom saw the Camera Club booth. "I can use my new camera in that club. I'm going to sign up here," he said.

Hector said, "I'll look around some more."

Hector looked at the Pet Club, the Music Club, and the Flower Club. Then he went to stand by the door.

Chapter 2

Ms. Cooper saw Hector. She asked, "Which club did you join, Hector?"

"I didn't join any club," he answered. "I didn't see one I wanted to join."

"Maybe you can start your own club. Think about it and let me know," said Ms. Cooper.

That night, Hector thought and thought
about a new club.

Chapter 3

The next day, Hector told Ms. Cooper about his idea. "Will you help me start the new club, Ms. Cooper?"

Ms. Cooper smiled. "Yes, Hector. Make a sign and hang it in the hall."

The Book Club

Find out about this
new club.
Meet with Hector and
Ms. Cooper today
at 2:00.

The Book Club

A group gathered at 2:00. Hector told the class about the club. "Each month, someone will choose a book. We'll all read the book. Then we'll meet and talk about it."

Everyone liked the idea. Hector signed up
ten club members.

"Good job, Hector," said Ms. Cooper. "The
Book Club is just what Morris School needed!"